INTENDED FOR MATURE AUDIENCES

C000007151

CONTENTS

DO YOU LIKE...
FISH STICKS?

© 2012 Comedy Partners. All Rights Reserved.
SOUTH PARK and all related titles, logos and
characters are trademarks of Comedy Partners.

Pedigree®

Published 2012.
Pedigree Books Limited, Beech Hill House, Walnut Gardens, Exeter, Devon EX4 4DH
www.pedigreebooks.com | books@pedigreegroup.co.uk

The Pedigree trademark, email and website addresses, are the sole and exclusive
properties of Pedigree Group Limited, used under licence in this publication.

ELEMENTARY
SCHOOL MUSICAL

HEAVEN VS. HELL

CARTMAN BURGER

SMUG ALERT!

£7.99

STAN MARSH

WHOA, I DON'T TAKE DRUGS AND WORSHIP SATAN!

THE LEADER AND NORMAL ONE OF THE GROUP, STAN IS OFTEN THE PEACEKEEPER. EMBARRASSED BY HIS FATHER AND BEATEN BY HIS SISTER, HE'S BEST FRIENDS WITH KYLE AND LEARNS SOMETHING EVERYDAY.

MOVIES

SHUT UP FAT ASS!

COME ON, EVERYBODY, BE PEOPLE NOW.

MOUNTAIN SCOUTS

WHATEVER...
I'LL DO WHAT I WANT!

FATBEARD

THE LAST OF
THE MEHEECANS

YEAH I WANT SOME
CHEESY POOFS!

8

ERIC CARTMAN

THE CRUEL, OBESE ONLY CHILD OF SINGLE MOTHER LIANE, CARTMAN IS SPOILT WITH JUNK FOOD. OPINIONATED, OBNOXIOUS AND MULTILINGUAL, HE OFTEN USES HIS ADVANCED INTELLIGENCE IN RESPONSE TO KIDS TEASING HIM ABOUT HIS WEIGHT.

SCREW YOU GUYS, I'M GOING HOME.

9

KICKASS, DUDE!

LIVING WITH HIS OVERPROTECTIVE MOTHER, LAWYER FATHER AND ADOPTED BROTHER, SIR IKE, KYLE IS THE SMART ONE OF THE GROUP. EVERYONE MAKES FUN OF HIM BECAUSE HE'S JEWISH AND HE LOVES PLAYING WITH "IMAGINARY" FRIEND MR. HANKY THE CHRISTMAS POO

KYLE BROFLOVSKI

OH MY GOD, THEY KILLED KENNY!

LIVING IN POVERTY WITH HIS REDNECK FAMILY, KENNY HAS AN ORANGE PARKA TIGHTLY AROUND HIS FACE, MAKING HIS SPEECH MUFFLED TO THE NORMAL EAR BUT CLEAR TO THE PEOPLE OF SOUTH PARK. HAS A SUPERHERO ALTER EGO NAMED MYSTERION.

KENNY McCORMICK

BUTTERS STOTCH

BUTTERS IS A NERVOUS SOCIAL OUTCAST
AFTER THE GROUP OUSTED HIM FOR TWEAK
TWEAK. CARTMAN'S CONSTANT TEASING OF THIS
ONLY CHILD HAS LED TO HIS EVIL ALTER EGO
PROFESSOR CHAOS.

OO-LOO-LOO I GOT
SOME APPLES

AWW HAMBURGERS...

THAT'S ME!

OHH, I'M GETTING STEAMED NOW!

SOUTH PARK

15

THE RESIDENTS OF SOUTH PARK

DON'T KILL KENNY!

SWEEEEEET!

LIFE IS ONLY PAIN

BLAME CANADA!

I'M SO STARTLED!

ERIC ISN'T FAT, HE'S BIG-BONED

VOTE OR DIE!

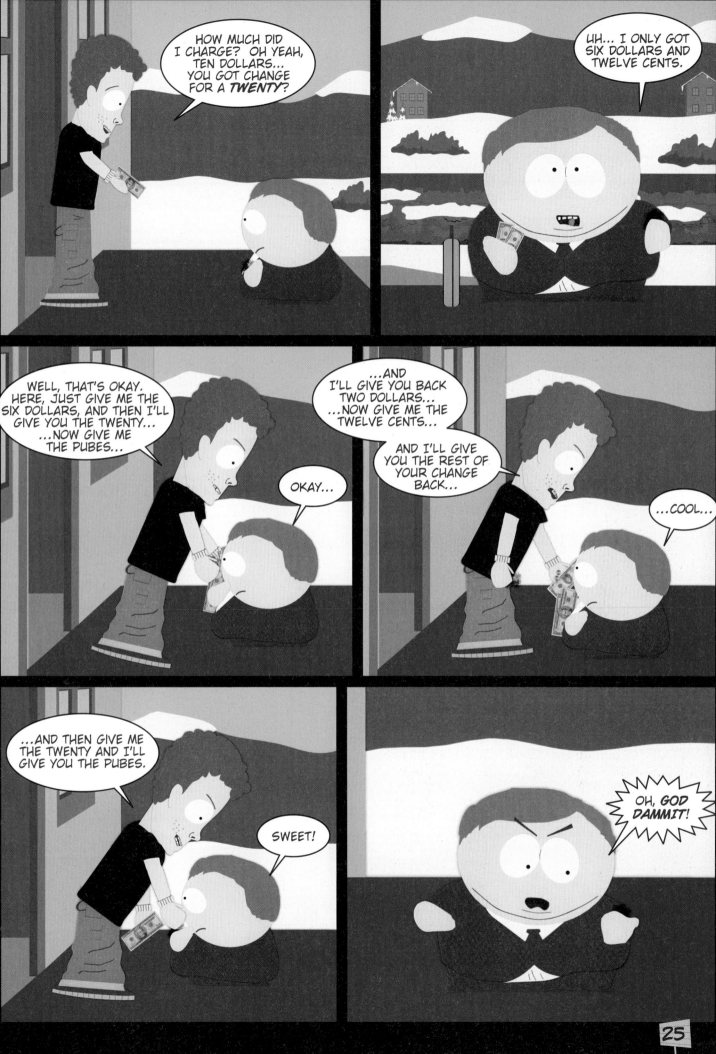

HE IS *NOT* SMARTER THAN ME! HE JUST *CHARMED* ME, THAT'S ALL. HE'S A *CHARMER*, THAT SCOTT TENORMAN, BUT I'LL *GET HIM SOMEDAY!*

CARTMAN... CAN I GIVE YOU SOME *ADVICE?*

JUST *LET IT GO*, DUDE. YOU'RE ONLY OUT SIXTEEN DOLLARS AND TWELVE CENTS! COUNT YOUR LOSSES AND MOVE ON. HE'S *SMARTER* THAN YOU!

ONE, PLEASE.

ONE, PLEASE.

MRPH, MRPH.

ONE, PLEASE.

FIVE BUCKS A HAIR? THAT'S LIKE A MILLION DOLLARS!

HERE, TAKE YOUR MONEY!

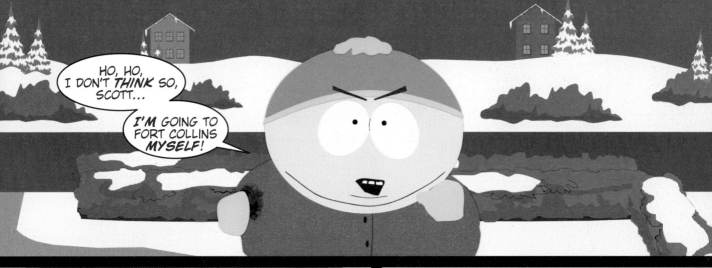

HO, HO, I DON'T THINK SO, SCOTT...

I'M GOING TO FORT COLLINS MYSELF!

YOU CAN'T DO THIS TO ME! NOOOOO!

HA HA! TOO RIGHT YOU ARE, SCOTT!

HAVE YOU NO HEART?

Ft. Collins

BUS TERMINAL

HAHAHA! WHAT A STUPID ASSHOLE!!

HOHOHO! ONE MILLION DOLLARS!!!

34

37

40

44

45

THAT NIGHT...

OKAY, WELL – IT LOOKS LIKE *EVERYONE'S* HERE!

LET'S PLAY THE *VIDEO*, SHALL WE?

BZzzT!

....WELCOME BACK TO *MTV*.

WE'RE HERE WITH THE MEMBERS FROM *RADIOHEAD*, PROBABLY THE HOTTEST BAND IN THE WORLD RIGHT NOW. GUYS, WHEN IS YOUR NEXT ALBUM COMING OUT?

THAT'S AN INTERESTING QUESTION, KURT.

BUT FIRST I'D JUST LIKE TO SAY THAT I REALLY I HATE THIS KID NAMED *SCOTT TENORMAN.* HE'S *STUPID.*

YEAH, *I* HATE SCOTT TENORMAN TOO.

I THINK *ALL* THE GUYS IN THE BAND HATE HIM! RIGHT, GUYS?

OH, *JESUS!* DID YOU *HEAR* THAT, SCOTT?

AND WILL THERE BE A NEW TOUR?

WELL, WE *WOULD* TOUR, BUT WE JUST HATE THAT SCOTT TENORMAN KID SO MUCH THAT WE DON'T WANT TO.

YEAH, SCOTT TENORMAN IS TOTALLY *NOT* COOL. HE IS *NOT COOL.*

WOW... THAT REALLY SUCKS FOR YOU, SCOTT! SCOTT?

LADIES AND GENTLEMEN, BOYS AND GIRLS...

HA HA!!! DID YOU SEE THAT?! SCOTT MUST HAVE RAN HOME *SO EMBARRASSED!*

HA HA! AND YOU KNOW WHAT? THAT WASN'T REALLY RADIOHEAD TALKING! I JUST *DUBBED THEIR VOICES OVER!* WHAT A *RETARD!!!* AND *EVERYONE SAW IT...*

IT'S TIME FOR... *THE AMAZING PUBE BOY!!!!*

I'M A LITTLE PIGGY, HERE'S MY SNOUT. OINK OINK OINK...

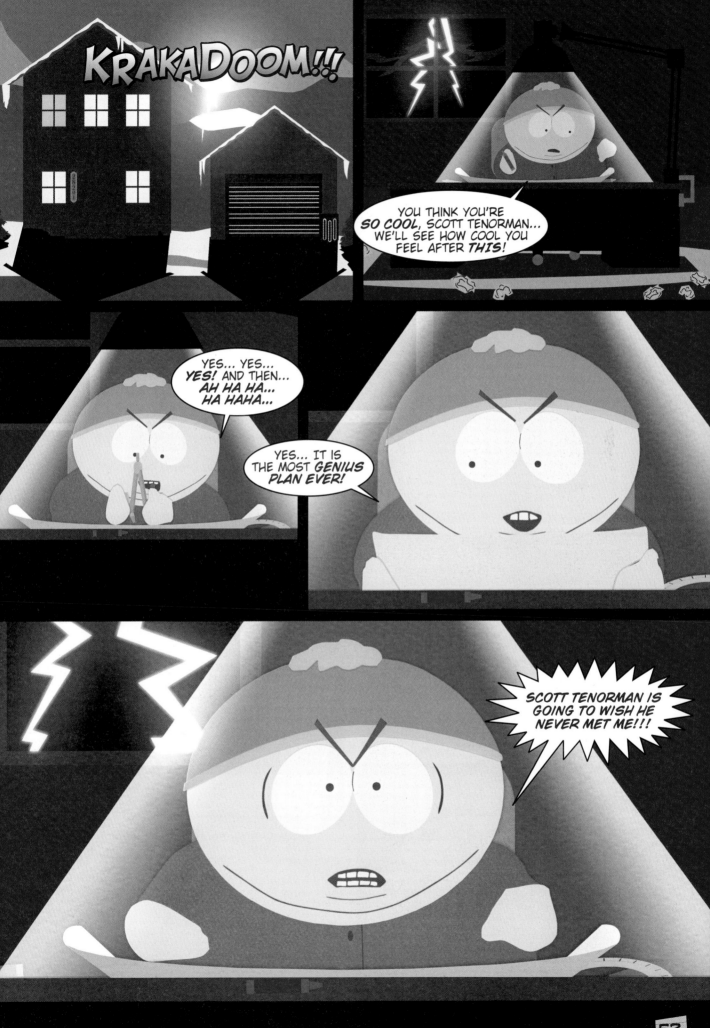

KRAKADOOM!!!

YOU THINK YOU'RE
SO COOL, SCOTT TENORMAN...
WE'LL SEE HOW COOL YOU
FEEL AFTER *THIS!*

YES... YES...
YES! AND THEN...
AH HA HA...
HA HAHA...

YES... IT IS
THE MOST *GENIUS*
PLAN EVER!

SCOTT TENORMAN IS
GOING TO WISH HE
NEVER MET ME!!!

SCOTT TENORMAN?

WHAT DO YOU WANT?

WE JUST WANT TO *WARN* YOU. ERIC CARTMAN, THE FOURTH GRADER, IS GOING TO TRY TO *TRICK* YOU SOMEHOW INTO GETTING YOUR *WIENER* BITTEN OFF BY A *PONY* THAT LIVES AT DENKINS RANCH.

HOW DO YOU KNOW?

'CUZ WE'RE HIS FRIENDS.

THEN WHY ARE YOU TELLING ME?

'CUZ WE HATE HIM.

OH.

WE JUST THOUGHT WE'D LET YOU KNOW. SEE YA.

SEE YA.

CLICK!

DING DONG!!!

DING DONG

HELLO, SCOTT!

...HEY.

I WAS JUST STOPPING BY TO INVITE YOU TO MY *CHILI CON CARNIVAL.*

IT'S A CHILI COOK-OFF WITH *RIDES, EVERYONE'S* COMING, AND I WANTED TO DROP BY *YOUR* INVITATION *PERSONALLY!*

CHILI CON CARNIVAL!!

74

THE END!

Pedigreebooks.com

The UK's leading Annuals specialist